This book belongs to:

Name: ....

Age: ....

I live in a place called:

....

Editor: Lisa Carless **Designer:** Naomi Kosick
© Disney. First published in Great Britain in 2007 by Egmont UK Limited,
239 Kensington High Street, London W8 6SA. All rights reserved.
ISBN 978 1 4052 3180 0
1 3 5 7 9 10 8 6 4 2
Printed in Italy.

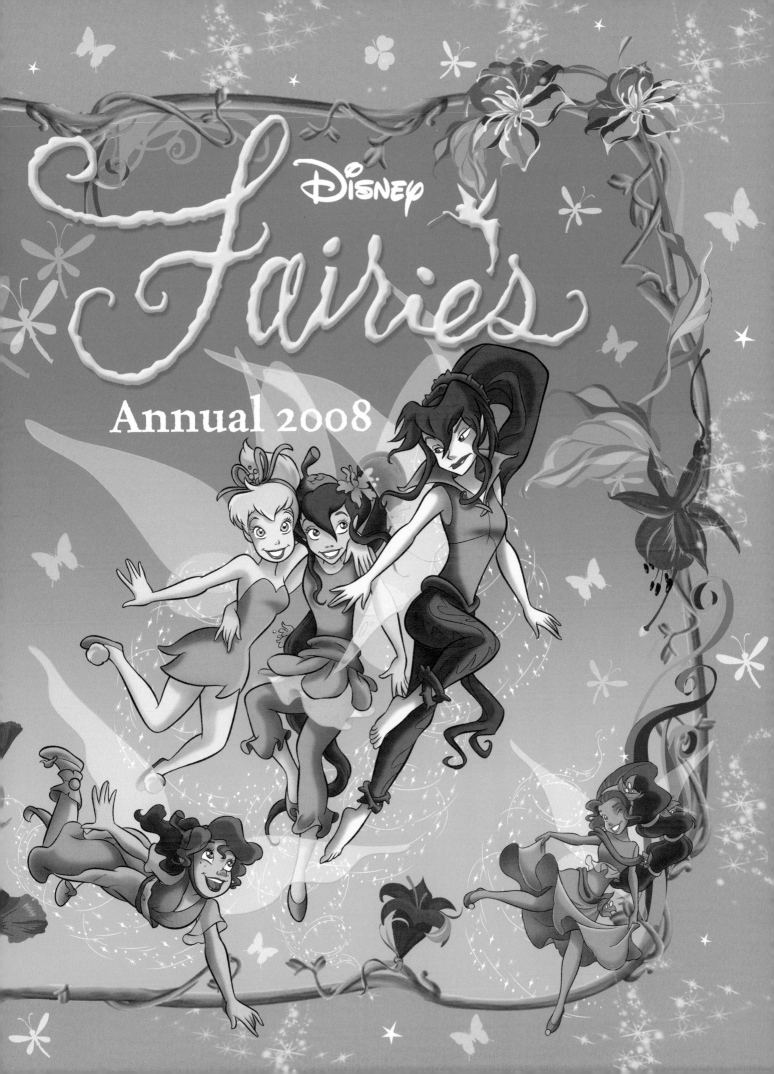

Welcome ...

... to the enchanting world of Pixie Hollow. In your Annual, you can join the fairies of Never Land as they fly off on exciting adventures! Have fun!

Disney Fairies

Inside the magic of Never Land ...

Welcome to Never

... and the enchanting world

Meet the main characters

Tinker Bell

Talent group: pots
and pans
Feisty Tinker Bell is one
of the handiest fairies in
Pixie Hollow. She loves to
tinker and fix things!

Prilla

Talent group: still
finding her way!
Prilla is the newest fairy
in Pixie Hollow and is
trying to find her talent!
Being young, Prilla is like
a playful Kitten!

Land ...
of Pixie Hollow

Lily

Talent group: garden
Lily is the green-fingered fairy of Pixie Hollow. She loves plants and knows when they are happy or sad.

Beck

Talent group: animals
Beck is kind of shy around other fairies - she prefers the company of animals and can talk their language!

Rani

Talent group: water
One of Tink's best friends, she's the only fairy who doesn't have wings. She does magical things with water.

Fira

Talent group: light
Fira lights up Pixie Hollow with her trained fireflies. She needs little catnaps to refuel because her talent can be exhausting!

Bess

Talent group: art
Bess is often splattered with paint because she loves creating things! Enchantingly enthusiastic, she is fascinated with colour.

Tinkflowers

Tinker Bell had fixed a pot belonging to Lily and was returning it to her ...

Lily? Lily, where are you?

I can't see you!

Here I am!

What are you doing in that hedge?

Combing it!

Eh? Why don't you give it a perm, as well?

Hey! What a great idea!

I was kidding, Lily!

11

12

Over there are some cloudflowers. Hey, look! A flowerflower!

Oh? What does it do?

It turns to face all the other flowers! It's a very happy flower.

Hey ... what about this?

Oh, this one ... is a Tinkflower! I planted it with you in mind!

And?

It turns to face **you**!

Ok, you've convinced me! Flowers are interesting!

A few days later, Prilla pays a visit to Tinker Bell ...

I didn't know you were a gardening fan, Tinker Bell!

Neither did I! But someone taught me that there's more to flowers than meets the eye!

The end

Which fairy?

Which fairy will reach Tink? Follow the ribbons through the maze to find out.

Beck

Start

Bess

Start

Rani

Start

Yay!

Finish

14

Spot the difference

These 2 pictures of Prilla may look the same but there are 8 differences in the bottom one. Can you spot them all?

Party time

Help Beck and Rani dance their way to the cake through the party balloons.

Start

1

2

3

4
Stop to talk to a squirrel. Back 1.

5

6

7

8

9

10
Spin around 3 times.

11

12

13

14

15
Run out of fairy dust. Back 3!

16

How to Play

You will need: a counter for each player and a die. Take it in turns to throw the die and move the counters around the board. Follow the instructions on the balloon you land on. The first player to reach the cake is the winner.

24 — Chase a butterfly. Take another turn.

25

23

26

22

27

21

28

29 — Tired wings! Back 10!

20 — Help Lily in the garden. Miss a go.

30 — Finish

19

17

18

Rainbow brooch

Help Bess to make and wear this brooch and you'll cast a beautiful rainbow wherever you go.

Note to parents: adult supervision is recommended when sharp-pointed items, such as scissors, are in use.

You will need:

Pink card

Gold cord

Beads

Scissors

Brooch Clasp

Sequins

Glue

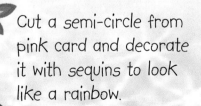

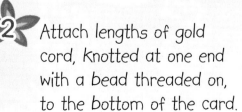

1 Cut a semi-circle from pink card and decorate it with sequins to look like a rainbow.

2 Attach lengths of gold cord, knotted at one end with a bead threaded on, to the bottom of the card.

3 Stick a brooch clasp to the back of the card and pin it on to your gown.

Bess says: Why not make a matching one to go in your hair?

19

The beautiful gift

One afternoon, Prilla was visiting Beck ...

Your room is so pretty, Beck! Really cosy ...

This is the thing I like best of all!

My feather bed has won you over, eh, Prilla?

No, this! Transforming a simple hazelnut shell into a candle holder was true genius!

This is not just any old nutshell! It is the most beautiful gift I have ever received ... I remember the day I got it, as if it were only yesterday ...

"It was an afternoon like any other. I was playing ball with my friends, the porcupines ..."

Oops!

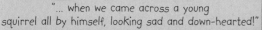

"... when we came across a young squirrel all by himself, looking sad and down-hearted!"

"It was his first time out in search of food, but ..."

... he hasn't found so much as one acorn all day! He doesn't want to disappoint his parents by coming home empty-pawed!

"The porcupines had a plan ... as sharp as one of their spines! They know the forest by heart!"

A big hazel tree? Just a short flight from here? Fantastic!

"There was a little problem to solve first ... make that three problems!"

The hazel tree is on the other side of Wough River. It's a long way on foot to the closest bridge ... and it's going to be dark soon!

21

"So, you know the underground tunnels that run through the forest?"

Yes, they're a real maze! Only animal-talent fairies can find their way down there!

Exactly! To get the tired squirrel there, I got him to chase the ball through all the tunnels ...

"... using them as a short cut!"

Run, squirrelly, run! Faster, faster!

"You should have seen his little face light up when we reached the tree!"

Excellent choice, little fellow!

"He gathered up all the nuts he could ..."

"Lots of hazelnuts for his parents and one ..."

... for me?

22

It was then that I understood that the most *beautiful* gift is one given with sincerity and affection.

Hey! It's getting dark outside!

Goodnight, Beck! Thanks for a great story!

Sweet dreams, Prilla!

Goodnight to you, too, little squirrel!

Beck's goodnight wish wafted out of her window ...

Beck's House

... through the forest and eventually all the way to ...

... the squirrels' nest where they were already having sweet dreams.

The end

Fairy puzzles

How quickly can you solve these magical puzzles?

1 Double trouble

Can you match up these tasty squirrel nibbles? Which one doesn't have a match?

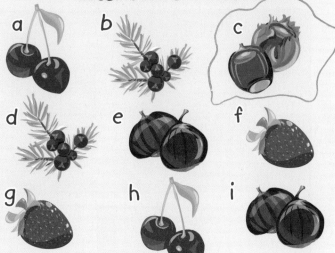

a   b   c

d   e   f

g   h   i

2 Spot the difference

Can you find the 5 changes in picture b?

a

b

③ Shadow sorting
Which shadow matches this pose of Prilla?

a

b

c

d

4 Coded message
Can you work out what the coded message says?

a b c d e f g h i j k l m

n o p q r s t u v w x y z

<u>d o</u>   <u>y o u</u>   <u>b e l i e v e</u>?

25

Animal friends

Beck just loves spending time with her animal friends in Never Land, especially the squirrels. Let's find out a bit more about these cute little creatures!

Squirrels don't hibernate but will stay in their nests if it's cold! They make nests high up in trees, out of twigs, leaves and moss. Sometimes, they will find a hole in a tree and build a nest in there.

Squirrels are very good climbers and love to hang upside down!

Look at this one enjoying a peanut! Yummy! Squirrels love acorns as well.

Colour Fira

Using your pens, pencils or crayons, add some pretty colours to Fira.

Memory game

Here's a game for you to play with Prilla. Study all the objects below for a minute and then cover them up. Now, see how many you can remember? Try it a few times and record your score each time.

How I scored:

1st go $\frac{9}{9}$

2nd go $\frac{7}{9}$

3rd go

Good friends

The Home Tree is bustling! Preparations are being made for the grand opening of a new terrace.

The carpenter-talent fairies are putting the finishing touches on their most recent creation ...

In Pixie Hollow, everyone lends a hand to decorate it ...

... everyone except Rani!

Sob! Sniff!

She's caught a terrible cold!

If I don't get better, I'll miss tonight's party! Sob, sniff!

... but I feel even worse, because I can't go to the party! Sob!

It's early to bed for Rani!

I've got to fall asleep quickly so I don't hear everyone else having fun!

But a persistent buzzing keeps Rani awake!

WAMP

Surprise!

Eh?

A circle of lightning bugs trained by Fira appeared ...

Hey! What's all this? I thought you were all on the new terrace!

... waterlilies were scattered all about the room ...

... and a mountain of melon-flavoured ice-pops were carried into Rani's room!

How to Play

You will need: a counter for each player and a die. Take it in turns to throw the die and move the counters around the board. Follow the instructions on the clouds that you land on. If you land at the bottom of some steps, climb up them. But if you land at the top of a slide, you have to slide back down. The first player to reach Bess is the winner.

21
Have an energy snack. On 5.

22

23

20

24

19

25
Beck urges you on. On 3.

18

26

16
Mend a pot. Back 2.

17

27

28

29

Finish

15

13

14

Which fairy are y

Answer each question below and total up how many as, bs, and cs you chose. Now, look to the right to see which fairy you are most like.

1

At a fancy-dress party, you would rather dress like:
a a cuddly bear ☐
b a sunflower ☑
c a paintbrush ☐

2

You relax by:
a taking a nature walk ☐
b arranging some flowers ☐
c painting a picture ☑

3

Your favourite day out would be:
a a trip to the zoo ☐
b a garden party ☑
c pottery making ☐

4

The word that you think best describes you is:
a motherly ☑
b patient ☐
c creative ☑

5

What would make you smile more?
a playing with a kitten ☑
b a bunch of flowers ☐
c a home-made present ☑

ou most like?

Mostly as

Beck

Just like Beck, you just adore animals. In fact, sometimes you prefer the company of animals to anything else! Fun and good-natured, you can also be a little bit shy.

Mostly bs

Lily

You have the green-fingered touch, just like Lily. You're a great listener who is kind and patient. You're as pretty as a daisy and as sunny as a daffodil - stay that way!

Mostly cs

Bess

Wow! You just love to be creative. You cannot stop painting and making things. You love to draw pictures for your friends and just adore being paint-splattered. Your enthusiasm rubs off on everyone!

6

Your friends turn to you when they:
a want to have some fun ☑
b need a good listener ☐
c need to be inspired ☐

7

Your clothes get dirty, you:
a hate being in a mess ☑
b don't mind too much ☐
c love it ☐

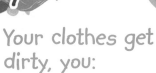

Waterlily bowl

Here's Rani to show you how to make a beautiful waterlily bowl.

Note to parents: adult supervision is required when sharp-pointed items, such as scissors, are used.

You will need:

Balloon

Pot pourri

Newspaper

PVA glue

Pencil

Paintbrush

Pink card

Crêpe paper

Scissors

Pink paint

1 Blow up a balloon, then glue on scraps of newspaper over half of it with watered-down PVA glue.

2 Leave the newspaper to dry, then pop the balloon. Cut out petal shapes from the hardened newspaper.

3 Paint the hardened newspaper with pink paint and leave to dry. Make a base for your bowl from pink card.

4 Stick the base to the bottom of your bowl, then fill the bowl with crêpe paper and pot pourri.

Rani says: Ask an adult to help you with the cutting.

39

Fira's light letters

Can you help Fira to find the words from the list in the wordsearch?

d	a	z	z	l	e	b	d
t	s	s	h	i	n	e	k
g	r	a	e	g	f	a	i
l	o	w	g	h	f	m	g
o	i	n	l	t	l	a	h
w	b	d	a	y	a	z	t
z	z	c	r	v	r	z	i
f	i	r	e	u	e	l	r

light
~~fire~~
~~day~~
~~glow~~
~~flare~~
~~beam~~
~~shine~~
~~glare~~
~~dazzle~~

Answers:

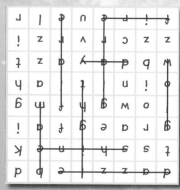

40

Do not disturb

With the breeze in her hair and the scent of flowers, there is nothing in the world that Lily likes more than breathing in nature!

She can watch a blade of grass growing for hours!

Bzzz

But something puts her patience to the test ...

Oh, hi, Mr. Bumble Bee! Nice day, isn't it?

Bzzz

Perfect for buzzing off ... away from here, don't you think?

Bzzz

Lily follows the bee all the way to Havendish Stream.

Thanks, pal! Good job!

Beck? What the ...?

Lily, at last! I sent Bumble out looking for you!

Bzzz

Beck explains that she couldn't leave the squirrels behind! Their parents had put her in charge of them for a while ...

... but that she needs Lily's help ...

... to save that plant?

That's right! With this high water, Havendish stream's likely to wash it away!

I thought that, maybe, with your green fingers ...

... and a pinch of fairy dust ...

Excellent! We managed to pull it up without hurting it!

And just in time! Well done, Lily!

Whoosh

43

Cute kittens

Beck loves spending time with animals and here are some cute kittens - one of her favourite animals.

Did you know that there are over 100 breeds of cat? Cats have 24 whiskers in total - four rows on each side.

When a cat drinks, its tongue scoops the liquid backwards! Slurp! When cats communicate with each other, they will almost never miaow!

Colour Tink

Using your favourite pens, pencils or crayons, add some pretty colours to Tink.

46

Fairy friends

Tink is waiting for a Fairy friend.
Which Fairy's path leads to her?

Lily

Fira

Vidia

Answer: Vidia's path

Magic fairy dust

Your dreams may come true with some fairy dust!

You will need:

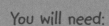
Small plastic bottle

Glitter glue pens

Paintbrush

Silver glitter

Purple paint

1 Clean a small plastic bottle, then paint the lid purple and leave to dry.

2 Draw a pretty design on the bottle with the glitter glue pens.

3 Carefully, fill the bottle with silver glitter and replace the lid.

Tink says: You have to believe in fairies for your fairy dust to work!

49

Without his help, I would never have been able to get everything I've fixed these past few days delivered!

Who is Tinker Bell talking about?

He takes fairy dust to each Fairy every day in Pixie Hollow! I'm sure he'd be pleased to count on another pair of wings!

Clunk

I'll go and give Terence a hand! Oops!

Phew! I almost *knocked* everything over! I really need to tidy up ...

... one of these days ... but not now!

Tinker Bell doesn't know that Terence got off to an early start this morning, too ...

... and headed straight for Tink's workshop!

Tinker Bell! You there?

And at Terence's home ...

Terence! Are you there?

Hey ... the handle of that teacup's broken!

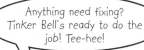
Anything need fixing? Tinker Bell's ready to do the job! Tee-hee!

BANG
BANG
BANG

And at Tink's home ...

What an airhead! I left in such a rush that ... I forgot to bring the most important thing!

Tink's House

51

Colour Beck

Using your colouring pens, pencils or crayons, colour in Beck. Tick the boxes next to the colours below that you used.

Squirrel search

Which path should Beck take through the maze to reach the squirrels?

a b c

Fastest first!

Play this game to see which one of Lily's friends, Fira or Bess, she will reach first.

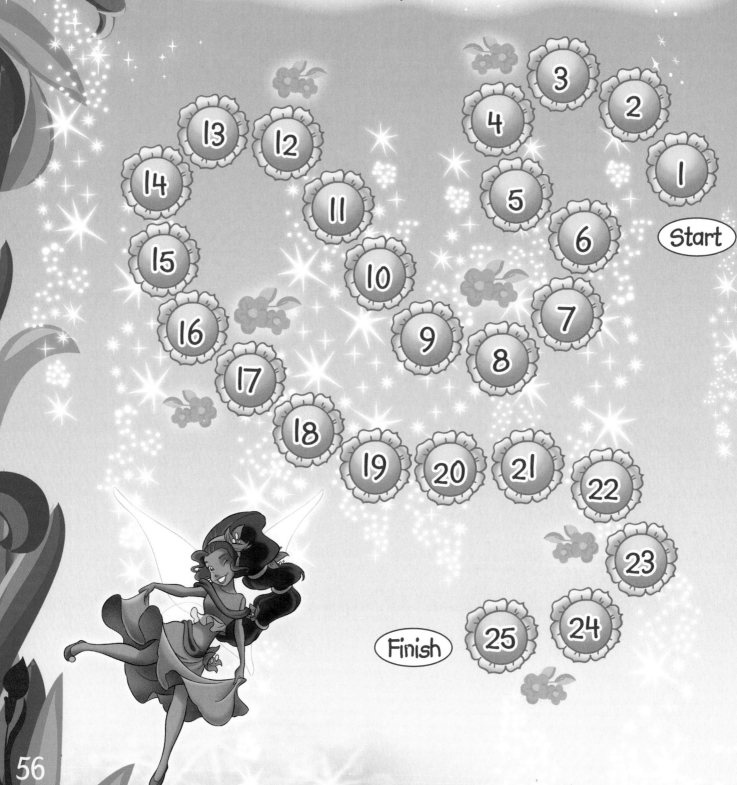

How to Play

This is a game for two players. You will need a die and two counters. First choose which fairy you are aiming for. The players take it in turns to throw the die. When a player throws an even number, she moves her counter forwards two flowers. But if a player throws an odd number, she moves her counter back one flower. The first player to reach the finish is the winner.

Start

3 4 2 5 1 6 9 7 10 8 11 12 19 18 17 13 20 16 14 21 15 22 23 24 25 Finish

57

A relaxing hairdo

There's a Fairy for every talent ...

Hey, Vidia! You could at least say thanks!

... some are handy in the Kitchen ...

Thanks, Dulcie, dearest!

... some fly fast and some work wonders with hair ...

Great, Tess! You've got a real talent for hairdressing.

Ah, come on!

It's true!

The end

Dot-to-dot

Join the dots to reveal a very handy and talented fairy!

61

Fit the bits

Which of the 8 close-ups can you find in the big picture? Which piece doesn't belong?

1 **2** **3** **4**

5 **6** **7** **8**

Answer: Piece 8 doesn't belong

Tink's thoughts

Tink likes to write down her fairy wishes in her diary every night. Do you have any fairy wishes? Write or draw them in the space below.

My fairy wishes are ...

Who am I?

Solve the riddle to see which fairy's name to write in the answer box.

My first is in Fairy but not in dairy,
My second is in Tink but not in tank,
My third is in rook but not in Hook,
My fourth is in hair but not in heir.

Write your answer here:

f i r a

64

Light naps

Deep into the night, preparations are underway for The Great Dance Festival in just a few days. All the fairies are extremely busy ...

... but the busiest are the ...

... light-talent fairies!!

Good job, my little friends! I'm proud of you!

CLAP CLAP

Our light games promise to be truly amazing this year!

Tomorrow night we'll have another rehearsal!

Yawn! I can't wait to get a good night's sleep!

When the light-talent fairies use their talent ...

Zzzz

... they need lots of rest to build their energy back up!

At the rehearsal the next night, Fira kept falling asleep ...

Zzzz

Huh? Sorry, Lily! I must have dozed-off! What were you saying?

I was showing you the freshly bloomed flowers for the party!

Poor Fira! During breaks between lighting rehearsals, her friends try to involve her in their preparations, but every time ...

Ready for the grand finale?

As ready as I'll ever be ... yawn ...

Water pinwheels!

Luckily, the evening of the Festival is soon here ...

... and what a success it is!

The next day, Fira enjoys a well-deserved rest ...

... and that evening she and her friends are finally free to spend a little time together!

... today all I did was SLEEP! What about you?

I spent the entire afternoon fixing this pot ...

Do you like it? If you want, you can use it as a vase!

... for these flowers, which I've prepared especially for this evening!

Oh, thanks girls! They're wonderful!

67

Well, what do you think? I've been working on it all day!

A gift, for you! It'll add a touch of colour to your room ...

And here's a tasty snack – the juiciest berries of the forest ...

... it took me and my animal friends hours to find them!

Slurp! Juicy idea, Beck! They'll give us a boost of energy for a long evening of chit-chat!

Huh?

Forget that! Tiring day, eh? I know how they feel!

Snore

Zzz

Sweet dreams, fairies!

The End